"Scat!" Said the Cat

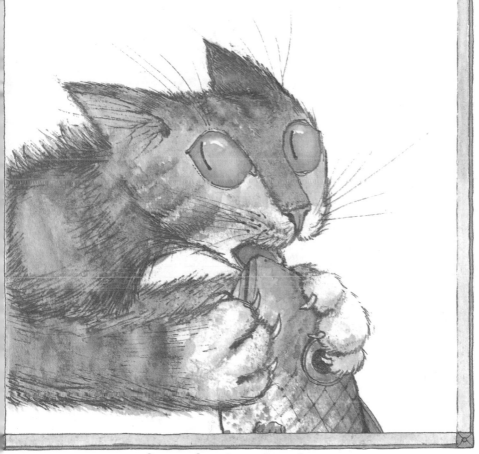

Story by Joy Cowley

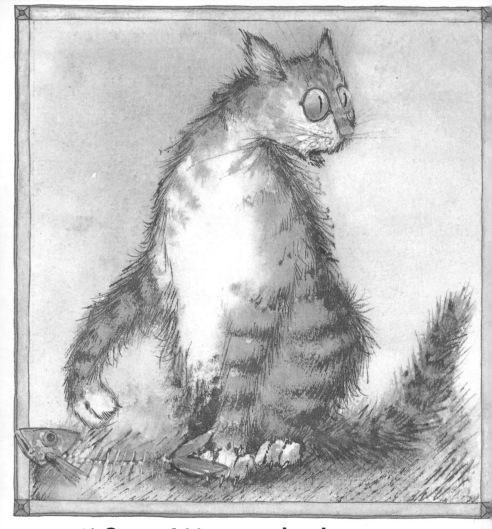

"Scat!" said the cat.

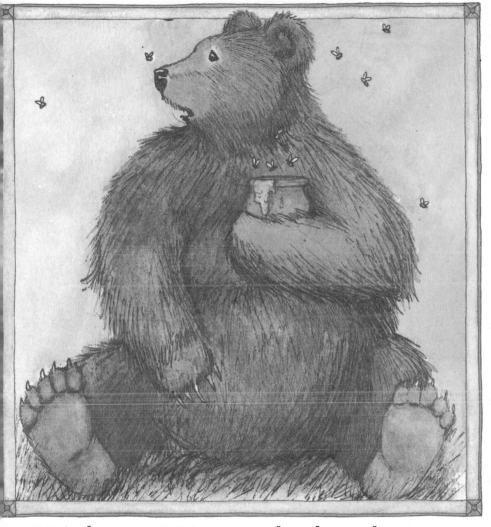

"Where?" said the bear.

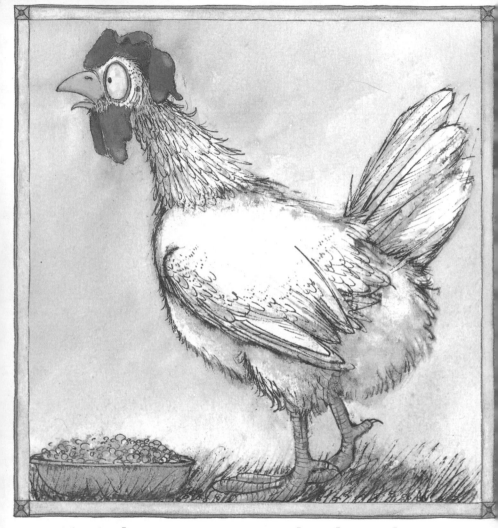

"When?" said the hen.

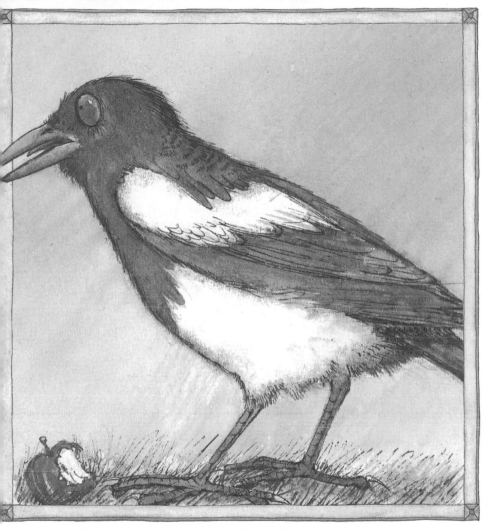

"Why?" said the magpie.

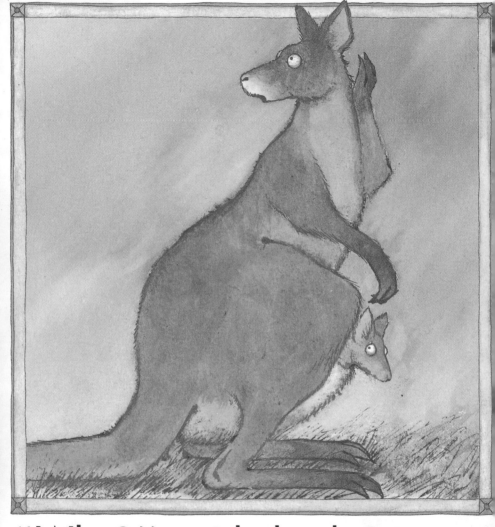

"Who?" said the kangaroo.

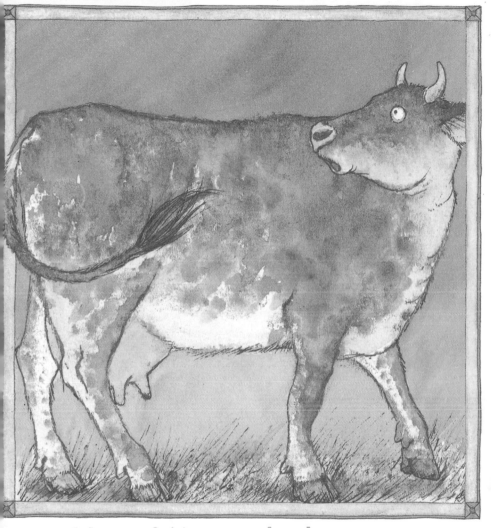

"How?" said the cow.

7

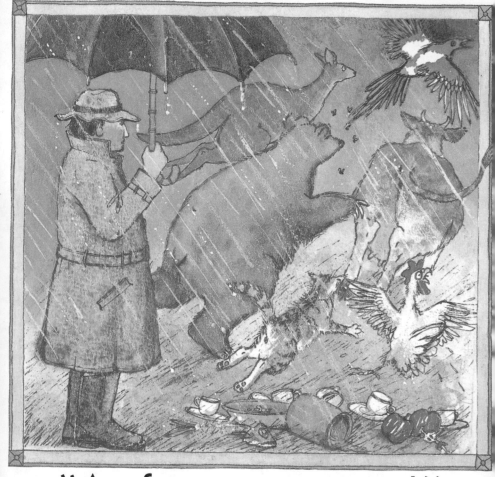

"As fast as you can!"
said the weather man.